2 EITHER

(a) Write a rhythm on one note, with time signature and bar-lines, to fit these
    Write each syllable under the note or notes to which it applies.

> Then, through the vast and gloomy dark,
> There moves what seems a fiery spark.   *Edward Lear*

Rhythm _____

Words   ....

Rhythm _____

Words   ....

OR

(b) Write a complete four-bar rhythm in $\frac{12}{8}$ time using the given opening.

3

3 Look at this extract from a piece by Finzi and then answer the questions that follow.

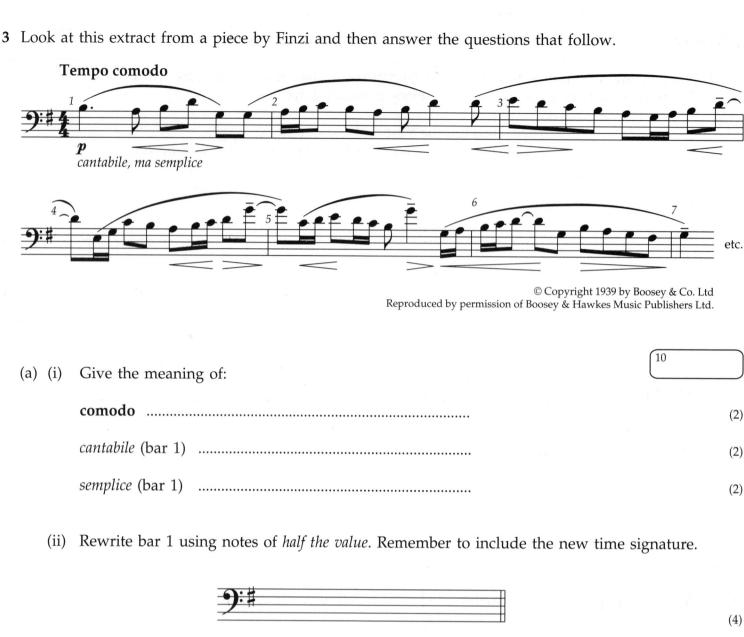

(a) (i) Give the meaning of:

comodo .... (2)

cantabile (bar 1) .... (2)

semplice (bar 1) .... (2)

(ii) Rewrite bar 1 using notes of *half the value*. Remember to include the new time signature.

(4)

(b) (i) Draw a circle around three notes next to each other that form the tonic triad of G major. (2)

(ii) Which other key has the same key signature as G major? .... (2)

(iii) Rewrite the first two notes of bar 4 so that they sound at the same pitch, but using the alto clef. Remember to put in the clef and the key signature.

(4)

(iv) Answer TRUE or FALSE to the following statement:
Every bar in the melody has a different rhythm. .... (2)

(c) (i) Name a member of the standard orchestral string family which could play this melody so that it sounds at the same pitch.

[10]

....

(2)

(ii) Name the highest sounding member of the standard orchestral string family.

....

(2)

(iii) Name two standard orchestral instruments, one woodwind and one brass, that normally use the bass clef.

Woodwind   ....

(2)

Brass   ....

(2)

(iv) Answer TRUE or FALSE to the following statement:

A timpanist might be asked to play 'arco'. ....

(2)

4 (a) Write the key signature of A♭ major and then one octave **descending** of that scale. Use semibreves (whole notes) and begin on the tonic.

[10]

(b) Add sharps or flats to the notes that need them to form the scale of B♭ **melodic** minor. Do *not* use a key signature.

5

5 Describe fully each of the numbered and bracketed melodic intervals in this extract (e.g. major 2nd, perfect 8ve).

Intervals:

1 ....

2 ....

3 ....

4 ....

5 ....

6 Add the correct rest(s) at the places marked ✱ to make each bar complete.

Theory of

Music

Exams

GRADE 4

2010

Theory Paper Grade 4 2010 A

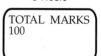

Duration 2 hours

TOTAL MARKS
100

This paper contains SEVEN questions, ALL of which should be answered.
Write your answers on this paper – no others will be accepted.
Answers must be written clearly and neatly – otherwise marks may be lost.

1 Look at this melody by Quantz and then answer the questions below.

15

(a) Give the meaning of:

   Affettuoso ....   (2)

   > (e.g. bar 6) ....   (1)

(b) The key of the melody is D major. Draw a circle around a note that is *not* in this key.   (2)

(c) Name the ornament circled in bar 8. ....   (2)

(d) Rewrite bar 5, *without the ornaments,* in compound time but without changing the
     rhythmic effect. Remember to include the new time signature.

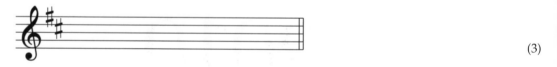

   (3)

(e) Write as a breve (double whole-note) an enharmonic equivalent of the second note of bar 1.

   (2)

(f) A square bracket (⌐‗‗‗‗‗‗¬) has been drawn over the first phrase.
     Mark all the other phrases in the same way.   (3)

2

7 (a) Name each of the numbered chords as tonic (I), subdominant (IV) or dominant (V). [15]
    The key is G major.

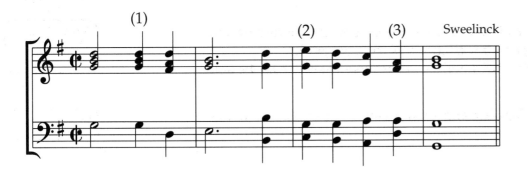

Chord:

(1) ....

(2) ....

(3) ....   (9)

(b) Add the correct clef and any necessary sharp or flat signs to make the triads named below.
    Do *not* use key signatures.

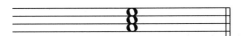 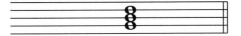 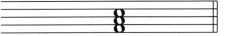

Key:	F♯ minor	G minor	D major
Triad:	dominant	tonic	subdominant

(6)

Theory Paper Grade 4   2010   B

Duration 2 hours

This paper contains SEVEN questions, ALL of which should be answered.
Write your answers on this paper – no others will be accepted.
Answers must be written clearly and neatly – otherwise marks may be lost.

DO NOT PHOTOCOPY
© MUSIC

TOTAL MARKS
100

1 Look at this melody by Tchaikovsky and then answer the questions below.

15

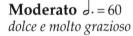

(a) Give the meaning of:

♩. = 60 .... (2)

grazioso (bar 1) .... (2)

riten. (bar 19) .... (2)

(b) The melody begins in the key of G major.
Which major key uses all the notes of bars 19–20? .... (2)

(c) Rewrite bar 1 so that it sounds at the same pitch, but using the alto clef.
Remember to include the key signature.

(3)

(d) A square bracket (⌐————————¬) has been drawn over the first phrase.
Mark all the other phrases in the same way. (4)

2 EITHER

(a) Write a rhythm on one note, with time signature and bar-lines, to fit these words. Write each syllable under the note or notes to which it applies.

> A man of words and not of deeds
> Is like a garden full of weeds.   *Anon.*

Rhythm _____

Words ....

Rhythm _____

Words ....

OR

(b) Write a complete four-bar rhythm in $\frac{3}{4}$ time using the given opening.

3 Look at this extract from a symphony by Brahms and then answer the questions that follow.

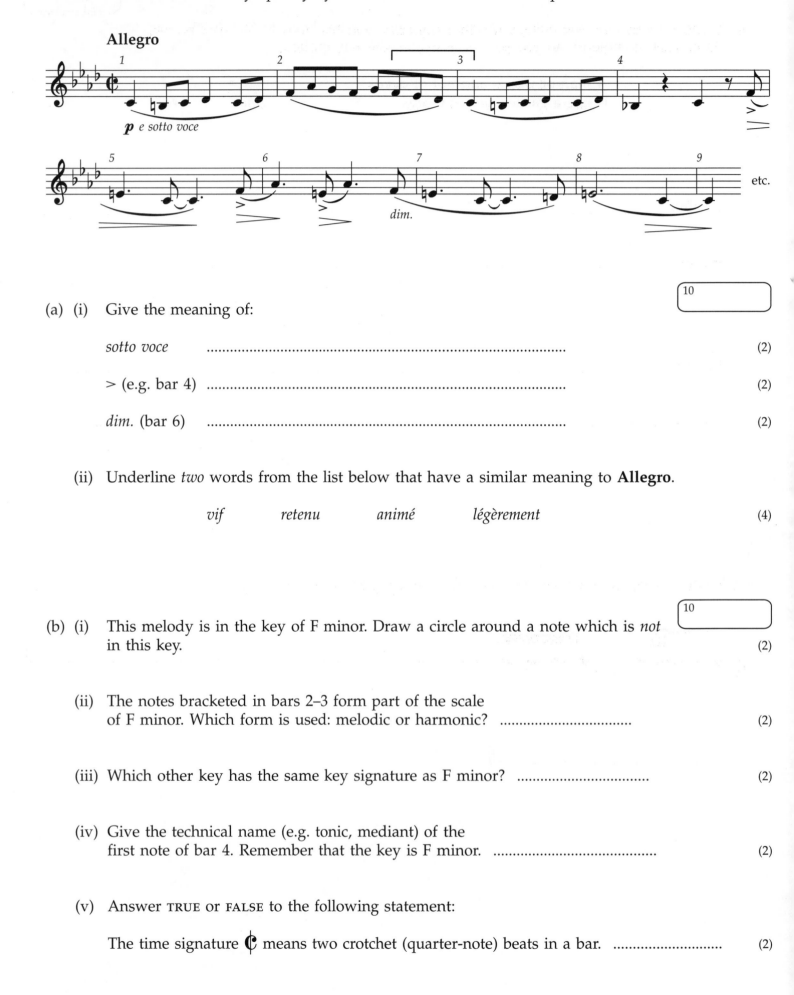

(a) (i) Give the meaning of:

sotto voce .... (2)

> (e.g. bar 4) .... (2)

dim. (bar 6) .... (2)

(ii) Underline *two* words from the list below that have a similar meaning to **Allegro**.

vif   retenu   animé   légèrement   (4)

(b) (i) This melody is in the key of F minor. Draw a circle around a note which is *not* in this key. (2)

(ii) The notes bracketed in bars 2–3 form part of the scale of F minor. Which form is used: melodic or harmonic? .... (2)

(iii) Which other key has the same key signature as F minor? .... (2)

(iv) Give the technical name (e.g. tonic, mediant) of the first note of bar 4. Remember that the key is F minor. .... (2)

(v) Answer TRUE or FALSE to the following statement:

The time signature 𝄵 means two crotchet (quarter-note) beats in a bar. .... (2)

10

(c) (i) Name two standard orchestral instruments, one woodwind and one brass, which could play this melody so that it sounds at the same pitch.

10

Woodwind .... (2)

Brass .... (2)

(ii) Underline *two* instruments from the list below which are members of the standard orchestral percussion family.

timpani   violin   cymbals   trumpet   (4)

(iii) Answer TRUE or FALSE to the following statement:
Double bass players may sometimes be asked to play 'con sordini'. .... (2)

4 (a) Write the key signature of five sharps and then one octave **ascending** of the **harmonic** minor scale with that key signature. Use semibreves (whole notes), begin on the tonic and remember to include any additional sharps, flats or naturals.

10

(b) Add all necessary sharp, flat or natural signs to the notes that need them to make a chromatic scale beginning on the given note.

5 Name each of these notes, as shown in the first answer.

B flat

....

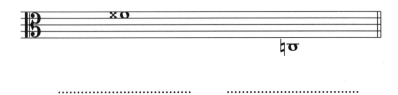

....

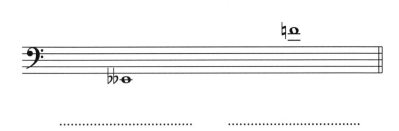

....

6 Describe fully each of the numbered and bracketed melodic intervals in this extract (e.g. major 2nd, perfect 5th).

Intervals:

1 ....

2 ....

3 ....

4 ....

5 ....

7 (a) Name each of the numbered chords as tonic (I), subdominant (IV) or dominant (V). [15]
The key is D major.

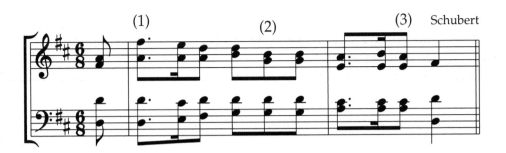

Chord:

(1) ....

(2) ....

(3) ....   (9)

(b) Write the named triads as shown by the key signatures.

         minor key   minor key   major key
            tonic   dominant   subdominant

(6)

Theory Paper Grade 4   2010   C

Duration 2 hours

This paper contains SEVEN questions, ALL of which should be answered.
Write your answers on this paper – no others will be accepted.
Answers must be written clearly and neatly – otherwise marks may be lost.

TOTAL MARKS
100

1 Look at this melody by H. Andriessen and then answer the questions below.

15

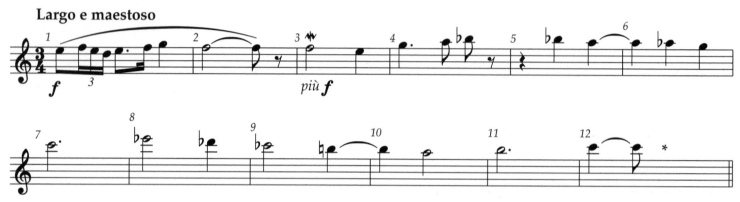

(a) Give the meaning of:

Largo .... (2)

maestoso .... (2)

più **f** (bar 3) .... (2)

(b) Draw a circle around four notes next to each other that form part of a descending chromatic scale. (2)

(c) Name the ornament used in bar 3. .... (2)

(d) Give the number of a bar which contains a note *and* its enharmonic equivalent. Bar .... (2)

(e) Add the correct rest(s) at the place marked ∗ to complete the final bar. (2)

(f) How many demisemiquavers (32nd notes) is the first note of bar 4 worth? .... (1)

2 EITHER

(a) Write a rhythm on one note, with time signature and bar-lines, to fit these words.
Write each syllable under the note or notes to which it applies.

> Where lies the land to which the ship would go?
> Far, far ahead, is all her seamen know.   *A. H. Clough*

Rhythm _____

Words ....

Rhythm _____

Words ....

OR

(b) Write a complete four-bar rhythm in $\frac{6}{8}$ time using the given opening.

3 Look at this extract from an orchestral piece by Smetana and then answer the questions that follow.

Allegro poco vivo, ma non troppo

etc.

(a) (i) Give the meaning of:

vivo, ma non troppo .... (4)

con sordini (bar 1) .... (2)

> (e.g. bar 1) .... (2)

(ii) Underline *one* word from the list below that has a similar meaning to **Allegro**.

      cédez   *vif*   *douce*   *modéré* (2)

(b) (i) Describe fully the bracketed melodic
interval in bar 5 (e.g. major 2nd, perfect 8ve). .... (2)

(ii) Rewrite bar 4 in compound time but without changing the rhythmic effect.
Remember to include the new time signature.

(4)

(iii) Name a minor key that uses all the notes in bar 3. Key: .... minor (2)

(iv) Give the letter name of the *highest* note in the melody. .... (2)

(c) (i) Name a standard orchestral string instrument, which normally uses the bass clef, that could play this melody so that it sounds at the same pitch.

[10]

....

(2)

(ii) Which standard orchestral woodwind instrument normally uses the bass clef?

....

(2)

(iii) Name two standard orchestral percussion instruments, one (other than piano) that produces notes of definite pitch and one that produces notes of indefinite pitch.

Definite pitch ....

(2)

Indefinite pitch ....

(2)

(iv) Answer TRUE or FALSE to the following statement:

A viola player might be asked to play 'pizzicato'. ....

(2)

4 (a) Write one octave **descending** of the **melodic** minor scale that has the given key signature. Use semibreves (whole notes) and begin on the tonic.

[10]

(b) Add all necessary sharp, flat or natural signs to the notes that need them to make a chromatic scale beginning on the given note.

5 Transpose this melody *up* one octave, using the treble clef as shown.

10

Haydn

6 (a) Rewrite these alto clef notes at the same pitch but using the bass clef.

10

(b) Rewrite these treble clef notes at the same pitch but using the alto clef.

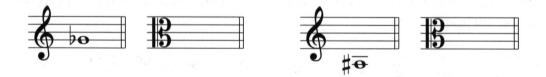

7 (a) Name each of the numbered chords as tonic (I), subdominant (IV) or dominant (V).
The key is A minor.

Chord:

(1) ....

(2) ....

(3) ....   (9)

(b) Identify these triads by naming the key and describing them as tonic (I), subdominant (IV) or dominant (V).

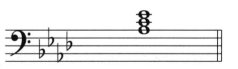

Key ....   Key ....   Key ....

Triad ....   Triad ....   Triad ....

(6)

Theory Paper Grade 4   2010   S

Duration 2 hours

This paper contains SEVEN questions, ALL of which should be answered.
Write your answers on this paper – no others will be accepted.
Answers must be written clearly and neatly – otherwise marks may be lost.

TOTAL MARKS
100

1 Look at this melody by Barsanti and then answer the questions below.

15

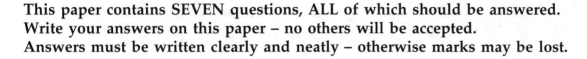

(a) Give the meaning of:

Non tanto allegro .... (3)

⌢ (e.g. bar 1) .... (1)

(b) Describe the time signature as: simple or compound ....

duple, triple or quadruple .... (2)

(c) Name the ornament used in bar 4. .... (2)

(d) Draw a circle around three notes next to each other that form the *dominant* triad of
B♭ major. (2)

(e) A square bracket (⌐‾‾‾‾‾‾‾‾‾‾‾‾¬) has been drawn over the first phrase.
Mark all the other phrases in the same way. (3)

(f) Rewrite the note marked ∗ in bar 3 so that it sounds at the same pitch, but using the
alto clef. Remember to include the key signature.

(2)

2 EITHER 10

(a) Write a rhythm on one note, with time signature and bar-lines, to fit these words. Write each syllable under the note or notes to which it applies.

> It was a chilly winter's night;
> And frost was glittering on the ground.   *William Barnes*

Rhythm _____

Words   ....

Rhythm _____

Words   ....

OR

(b) Write a complete four-bar rhythm in $\frac{4}{8}$ time using the given opening.

3 Look at this extract from an orchestral piece by Rossini and then answer the questions that follow.

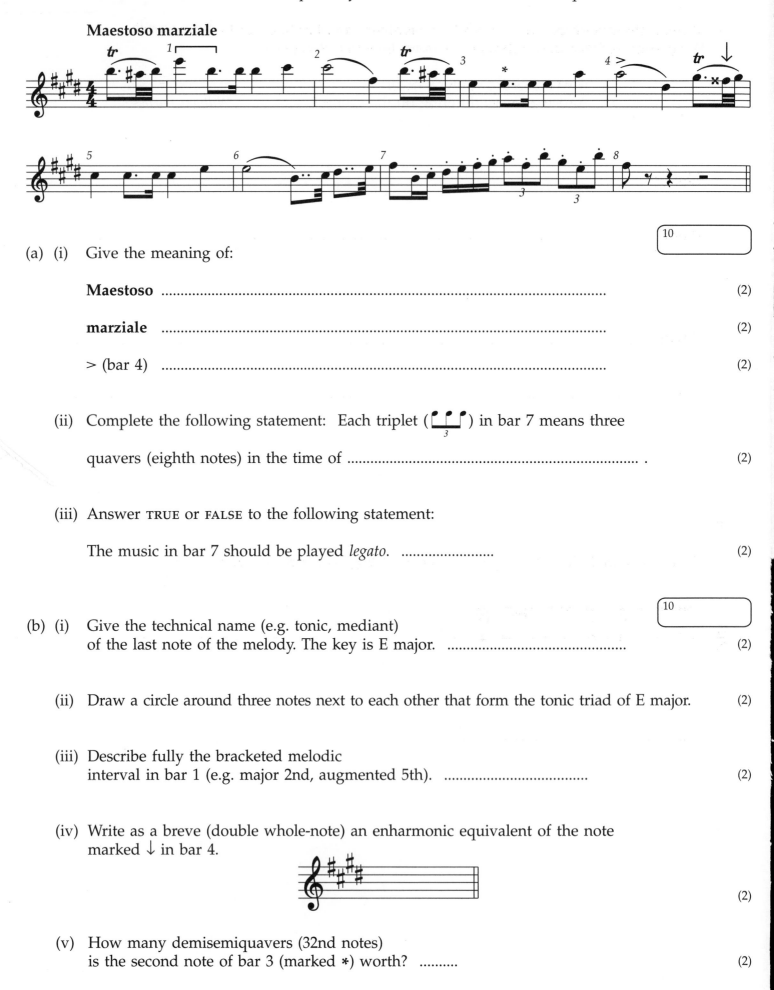

(a) (i) Give the meaning of:

   Maestoso .... (2)

   marziale .... (2)

   > (bar 4) .... (2)

   (ii) Complete the following statement: Each triplet ( ) in bar 7 means three

   quavers (eighth notes) in the time of .... (2)

   (iii) Answer TRUE or FALSE to the following statement:

   The music in bar 7 should be played *legato*. .... (2)

(b) (i) Give the technical name (e.g. tonic, mediant)
   of the last note of the melody. The key is E major. .... (2)

   (ii) Draw a circle around three notes next to each other that form the tonic triad of E major. (2)

   (iii) Describe fully the bracketed melodic
   interval in bar 1 (e.g. major 2nd, augmented 5th). .... (2)

   (iv) Write as a breve (double whole-note) an enharmonic equivalent of the note
   marked ↓ in bar 4.

   (2)

   (v) How many demisemiquavers (32nd notes)
   is the second note of bar 3 (marked *) worth? .... (2)

(c) (i) Name a standard orchestral woodwind instrument that
          could play this melody so that it sounds at the same pitch. .... (2)

(ii) Name the lowest sounding member
      of the standard orchestral brass family. .... (2)

(iii) Which member of the standard
       orchestral string family normally uses the alto clef? .... (2)

(iv) Underline *two* instruments from the list below that might be asked to play 'con sordini'.

          flute   horn   violin   triangle   (4)

4 (a) Write one octave **ascending** of the major scale that has the given key signature.   10
        Use semibreves (whole notes) and begin on the tonic.

(b) Write one octave **descending** of the scale of G♯ **harmonic** minor. Do *not* use a key signature but put
     in all necessary sharp or flat signs. Use semibreves (whole notes) and begin on the tonic.

5 Transpose this melody *down* one octave, using the bass clef as shown.

Corelli

6 (a) Rewrite these alto clef notes at the same pitch but using the treble clef.

(b) Rewrite these bass clef notes at the same pitch but using the alto clef.

7 (a) Name each of the numbered chords as tonic (I), subdominant (IV) or dominant (V). 15
 The key is G major.

Schumann

Chord:

(1) ....

(2) ....

(3) ....   (9)

(b) Write the key signatures and triads named below.

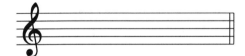 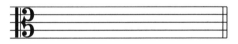 

Key: C♯ minor   B♭ major   A major
Triad: dominant   tonic   subdominant

(6)

Support material for ABRSM Music Theory exams

Theory of Music Exams 2010
Model Answers
Grades 1 to 8 (separately)

Music Theory in Practice
Grades 1 to 8 (separately)

Music Theory in Practice
Model Answers
Grades 1 to 5 (separately)

The AB Guide to
Music Theory
Parts I and II

First Steps in
Music Theory
Grades 1–5

ABRSM's mission is to motivate musical achievement. We aim to support the development of learners and teachers in music education worldwide and to celebrate their achievements. We do this through authoritative and internationally recognized assessments, publications and professional development support for teachers, and through charitable donations.

ABRSM
24 Portland Place
London W1B 1LU
United Kingdom

www.abrsm.org

Published by ABRSM (Publishing) Ltd,
a wholly owned subsidiary of ABRSM

Printed in England by Page Bros (Norwich) Ltd
01/12

ISBN 978-1-84849-289-9